# And Jesus Is Hi...

C. G.    Joyfully                                                    Handel

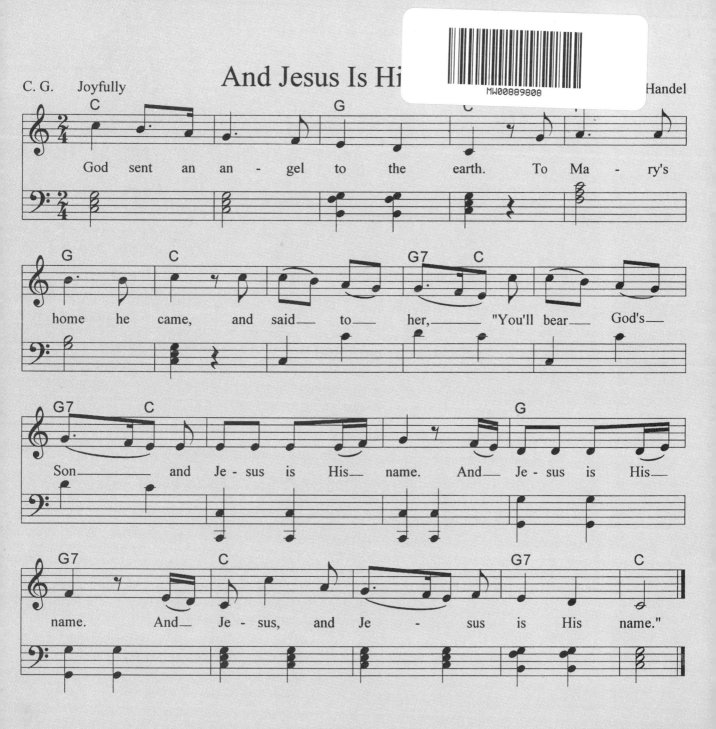

God sent an an - gel to the earth. To Ma - ry's

home he came, and said to her, "You'll bear God's

Son and Je - sus is His name. And Je - sus is His

name. And Je - sus, and Je - sus is His name."

# Joy to the World

Carol Greene

*Illustrated by Christopher Gray*

*The text of this book may be sung to the tune of*
*"Joy to the World."*

CPH
SAINT LOUIS

God sent an angel to the earth.
To Mary's home he came
And said to her,
"You'll bear God's Son
And Jesus is His name,
And Jesus is His name,
And Jesus, and Jesus is His name."

To sleeping Joseph, Mary's friend,
The angel came again.
"The holy Child
That Mary bears
Will save the world from sin,
Will save the world from sin,
Will save, will save the world from sin."

Mary and Joseph soon were wed.
Then came the order clear:
"We'll count you each
In your hometown."
And Mary's time was near,
And Mary's time was near,
And Mary's, and Mary's time was near.

So down the dusty road they went
To little Bethlehem.
But all the inns
Were filled up full.
There was no room for them.
There was no room for them.
There was, there was no room for them.

Darkness had settled thick and cold
When one innkeeper said,
"My stable lies
In back, my friends.
Go there and make a bed.
Go there and make a bed.
Go there, go there and make a bed."

Back in the stable Mary lay
And Joseph stood forlorn.
But safely in
That bed of straw
The Son of God was born,
The Son of God was born,
The Son, the Son of God was born.

Low in a manger slept the Child,
His tiny hands uncurled.
The watching beasts
Could hardly know
He'd come to rule the world,
He'd come to rule the world.
He'd come, He'd come to rule the world.

Out in the icy, starlit hills,
Poor shepherds watched their sheep
Or, wrapped in cloaks,
Lay on the ground
And slept a troubled sleep,
And slept a troubled sleep,
And slept, and slept a troubled sleep.

Then God's great glory filled the sky.
The shepherds shook with fear.
An angel spoke:
"I bring good news!
The Son of God is here.
The Son of God is here.
The Son, the Son of God is here.

Glad hosts of angels sang out then
And "Glory" was their song,
And "Peace on earth,
Good will to all!"
So sang the heavenly throng,
So sang the heavenly throng,
So sang, so sang the heavenly throng.

Quick ran the shepherds to the town.
Could such good news be true?
And when they saw
The Jesus Child,
The shepherds' hearts sang too,
The shepherds' hearts sang too,
The shepherds', the shepherds' hearts sang too.

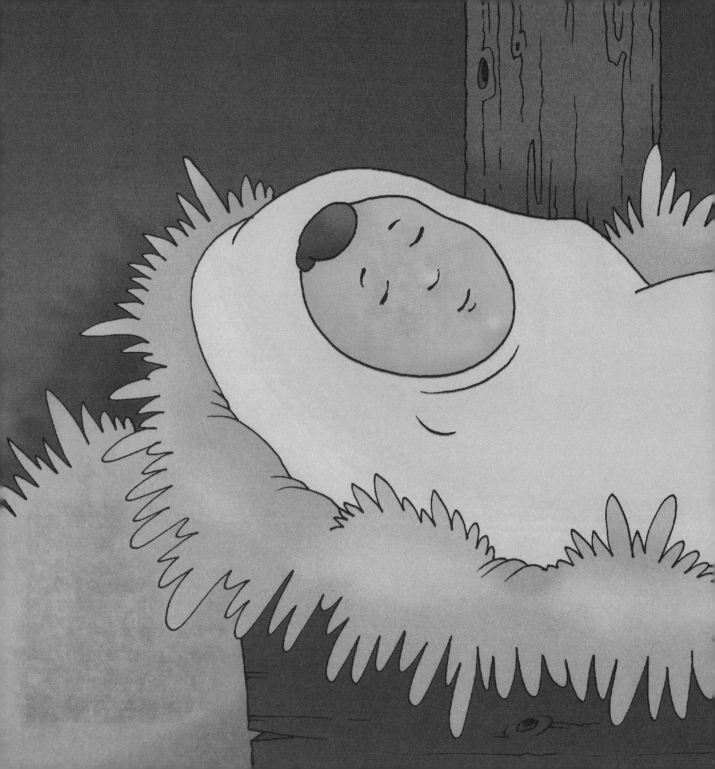

# And Jesus Is His Name